Bo

the Bear likes to collect machines and their parts. Let's check out his collection.

A is for airplane. Bo likes flying above the clouds.

B is for Baha Truck, jumping and bumping over the sand.

C is for car. Bo likes
all kinds of cool cars.

D is for dune buggy, doing donuts on the dunes.

E is for engine. Energy from an engine makes things go!

F is for fire truck. Can you help Bo find the frightened kitty?

G is for garbage truck, gobbling up garbage.

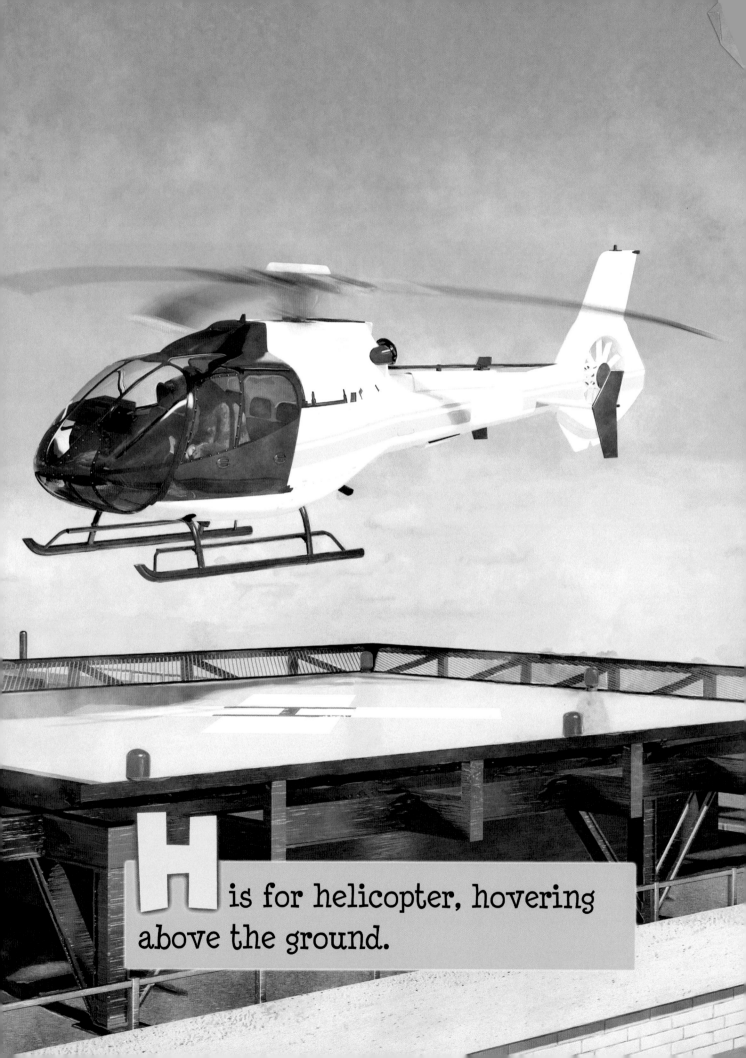

His for helicopter, hovering above the ground.

I is for industrial tractor. Inside and outside, Bo can pull heavy loads.

J is for Jet Ski, jumping the waves.

K is for kart. Bo keeps his wheels on the track when he drives his kart.

L is for lifeboat, launching from the lighthouse.

M is for motorcycle. Bo likes a motorcycle that moves smoothly.

N is for nuclear submarine. Bo never misses a chance to explore.

O is for orbiter, over the Earth and out into space.

P is for police car. Bo likes to help people keep the peace.

Q is for quad, never quiet, always loud.

R is for rocket, ready to reach the stars.

S is for sailboat. Bo the Bear loves the wind in his sails.

T is for truck. Bo uses tools to tune his trucks!

U is for ultralight aircraft, up, up, and through the air.

V is for van. VROOOOM, goes the van when Bo steps on the gas.

W is for wheels. Which wheels are the biggest?

X is for excavator, digging and excavating rocks and dirt.

Y is for yacht. Bo painted the yacht yellow just like his Monster Truck.

Z is for zipper truck, zipping and shifting cement blocks.

A

B

C

D

E

F

G

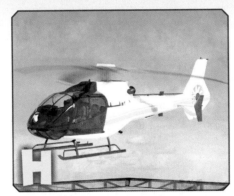

H

I

J

K

L

M

N

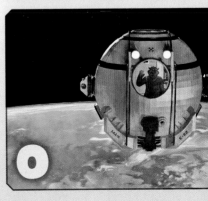

O

Can you name all of the letters of the alphabet? Do you remember the names of the machines and the parts in Bo's collection?

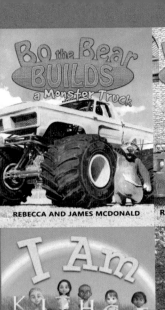

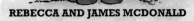
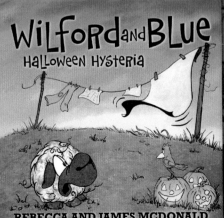
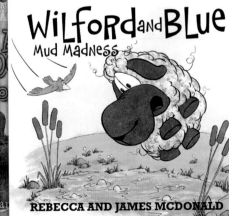